ERMA DOES
THE MATH

ANN STRAWN

ILLUSTRATED BY ANISHA

For George, Jerome, Lucy, Peter, Portia, Gertrude and Edward

"Hey, Aunt Erma, it's Tameka! Is it okay if I come in?"

"Come on in here, baby girl. Sweet Lawd! It's always a treat seeing you."

"Oh, Aunt Erma, I'm not a baby anymore. I brought you something for your birthday!"

"Do you know how old I am? Now, let's see, I was born in 1906. Take the present year and subtract 1,906. Great day! That makes me over 100 years old!"

"I know, Auntie. Why don't you open your gift?"

"Now you know better than that! First, you've got to sit down here and have one of my chocolate cupcakes. They're extra sweet today. I used almost 402 grams of sugar! Do you know how much that is?"

"I'm not sure, how many grams are in a cup?"

"A cup of white sugar is 201 grams, baby girl."

"Oh, that's right! 402 divided by 201, that's two cups of sugar. These cupcakes really are sweet! Are you ready to open your gift now?"

"How about you help your Auntie and hang this picture. I want it over the bookcase about two meters high. Do you know how high that is? I'll start you off, there's three feet in a meter."

"Three times two, about six feet.

"I don't remember ever seeing this picture before. They're all African American women. Where was this taken?"

"That was at Langley Air Force Base in Virginia. There's Mary Jackson, Katherine Johnson, and me. Great day! It had to be around 5 degrees Celsius then. Do you know how cold that is?"

"Argh! So much math! Isn't that what computers are for? And you still haven't opened your gift."

"You're lookin' at a computer, honey! I used to do math all day long. No such thing as looking it up, did it all by hand. Multiply 5 degrees Celsius by 1.8 and add 32. There's scratch paper on the table."

"Okay, so that comes out to 41 degrees Fahrenheit. That's cold. Did you really have to do this all day?"

"Took me a week to solve one problem. Filled up six notebooks. Look over in that drawer. The hammer and nails are in there. Now you be careful climbing up that step stool."

"I will, but then you need to open your gift! What kind of math problems took a week to solve? I'd give up after a minute."

"Not if you were sending someone to the moon! Do you know how many minutes are in a week? There's 60 minutes in an hour, multiply by 24 hours in a day."

"Let me concentrate on hammering first. Okay done. Hmm, multiply by 7 days in a week. That's 10,080 minutes. What were you saying about going to the moon?"

60 x 24 x 7
=10,080

I was part of the flight research team for NACA."

"Do you mean NASA? The National Aeronautics and Space Administration?"

"Up until 1958 it was NACA, National Advisory Committee for Aeronautics. That picture was taken around 1945. There were 25 of us at Langley then, doing all the math for the space missions. We worked on things like which jet fuels were best to get a rocket safely to the moon. Do you know how fast a rocket has to travel to get to outer space?"

"Wait, I remember this from science class! It's got to get away from Earth's gravity. That's 9.8 meters per second squared. A rocket would have to go faster than that. Whoa! You helped put people on the moon?"

You got it! They called us Human Computers, Black Computers and even Computers with Skirts. Great Day! I always thought that last one was funny! Katherine and I worked with the white engineers. That was during segregation, when black and white people weren't allowed to work together. But our calculations were so accurate that astronaut John Glenn himself wouldn't take off until we checked his trajectories.

"Come over here, sweet potato, let me show you something."

"Is it more math? What's a trajectory? Are you ready to open your gift now?"

"Look out the window, baby girl!"

"It's a full moon tonight, beautiful!"

"It takes three days to get there. Do you know where the moon will be three days from now?"

"What? Can I have a hint. How fast is the moon moving?"

"It's moving 3,683 kilometers per hour."

"Okay, but is the moon moving in a straight line? Isn't the Earth moving, too? Argh! Being a computer is hard!"

"You know what you don't know, that's a good start! Trajectories are flight paths. You see that constellation? That's Gemini. Three days from now the moon will be right next to it."

"Can we take a break, Auntie? You've got a birthday gift to open."

"Sweet Lawd! I almost forgot! What a beautiful pair of earrings, they look like the moon and stars! How did you know?"

"I didn't, but I've always loved the moon! Happy birthday, Aunt Erma!"

Author's Note

My great aunt Erma Tynes Walker was a Human Computer at the Langley Jet Propulsion Lab in Hampton, Virginia from 1943 until 1980. She worked alongside Katherine Johnson in the Flight Analysis Department calculating flight trajectories for the Mercury, Gemini and Apollo missions. At a time when African Americans faced many obstacles, Erma and her colleagues were an integral part of the space race. She loved math, but she also enjoyed sewing, baking and being with her many nieces and nephews. Erma will always be remembered as a smart, funny and sometimes quirky aunt.

Discussion Questions

1. It takes three days for a spaceship to fly to the moon. If you could go, what would you take with you?

2. How tall are you in inches? How tall are you in centimeters?

3. If you met a human computer what would you say to her?

4. What would you give a human computer for her birthday?

Author Website:

www.annstrawnbooks.com

Made in the USA
Columbia, SC
21 November 2020